boon

or

bane

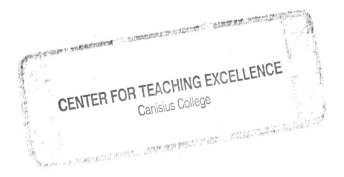

IIE Research Report Series Number 15

boon

or

bane

Foreign Graduate Students
in U.S. Engineering Programs

ELINOR G. BARBER, Institute of International Education
ROBERT P. MORGAN, Washington University

We gratefully acknowledge the grant from the National Science
Foundation which made this publication possible.

INSTITUTE OF INTERNATIONAL EDUCATION
809 UNITED NATIONS PLAZA, NEW YORK, N.Y. 10017

Contents

Foreword

The large and increasing percentage of graduate students in U.S. engineering schools who are foreign-born is a noteworthy development of the last decade. Opinions differ widely as to whether this phenomenon is beneficial to engineering schools, to the U.S. engineering profession, or to the nation. This study by Drs. Barber and Morgan contributes valuable data and analysis to the discussion of this issue.

There are some who consider the willingness of U.S. graduate schools of engineering to accept large numbers of graduate students, post-doctoral fellows, and visiting faculty members from foreign countries an act of folly. Their position is sometimes summarized in the phrase "we are educating our competitors."

There are others who feel that the ability of U.S. engineering schools to attract foreign graduate students is a tribute to their quality. From this point of view, the appropriate concern is that U.S. engineering schools continue to maintain a position of global leadership.

From a nationalistic perspective, the dependence of U.S. engineering schools on the foreign-born to maintain an adequate number of qualified graduate students and to supply the demand for engineering Ph.D. recipients by U.S. engineering schools and U.S. industrial companies is of concern. If federal government policy-makers are concerned about the nation's dependence on foreign sources of petroleum, should they not be deeply concerned about a growing dependence on foreign-born "brains" to supply our academic and industrial workforce requirements?

From still another point of view, there are those who attribute the strength of U.S. engineering schools to their ability to attract top-caliber students from all over the world. High quality graduate students and research assistants are essential to the creation of the lively intellectual environment characteristic of front-rank graduate schools.

Other aspects of this issue merit consideration. What is the effect on the country of origin of these students? If highly educated engineers return and find appropriate employment, the effect is clearly positive. Conversely, there may be a net loss to a country which has educated talented students through the baccalaureate degree only to have them emigrate and make their major contribution elsewhere.

Thus the issue of the large number of foreign-born engineering graduate students in the U.S. has many ramifications. This report examines a number of them and supplies significant data about the experiences and attitudes of the faculty members and department chairpersons who are the most directly involved.

F. Karl Willenbrock
Executive Director
American Society for Engineering Education

Introduction

Colleges and universities in the United States have for many years welcomed foreign students with positive expectations concerning the contributions these foreign students are likely to make to the quality of education and with only vague concerns that the economic costs of foreign students may outweigh the benefits. Since, overall, the proportion of foreign students currently constitutes less than 3 percent of the total population of students in U.S. institutions of higher education, it is not surprising that, as documented by Craufurd Goodwin and Michael Nacht in their study, [1], students from overseas are relatively insignificant among the problems that preoccupy educators. Goodwin and Nacht found that when campus officials or faculty do give some attention to the issue of foreign students, they tend to assume that foreign students add to the benefits imputed to diversity in student populations more generally. In the l980s, to be sure, with growing economic constraints afflicting universities, the issue of costs has acquired new salience; educators are now increasingly on the defensive with regard to the extent of the subsidies that foreign students allegedly receive and the share of financial aid that is provided to foreign students. At the same time, some efforts have been made recently to conceptualize the costs that foreign students entail given the present conditions in higher education generally as well as in particular kinds of institutions and particular fields of study [2].

In U.S. graduate engineering education, especially, benign indifference about the costs of foreign students and the "humanist presumption" [3] in favor of the educational contributions they make are under severe pressure because of the very high proportion of foreign graduate students. Although within the foreign engineering student population the proportion of graduate students declined from 47 percent in 1969/70 to 29 percent in 1979/80, the proportion of foreign students (on either temporary or permanent visas) among all students receiving doctoral degrees in engineering almost doubled during the same period. In 1981, according to National Science Foundation statistics,this proportion topped 50 percent, and it has remained above the 50 percent level ever since [4].

The uneasiness about engineering education that prevails these days among engineering educators has a number of sources, but it may be related at least in part to the role of the foreign students. In a recently completed study by the American Society for Engineering Education (ASEE) on the quality of engineering education [5], major attention was focused, among other things, on the poor condition of equipment and laboratories and on the weak design content of curricula. It is possible that tendencies toward the neglect of laboratories and of design may have been reinforced by the theoretical orientation of foreign graduate students which we shall discuss in a later section of this report. Yet the tilt toward the theoretical occurred prior to the recent strong increase in the proportion of foreign students. In any event, those favoring a stronger theoretical orientation are likely to look with favor on foreign graduate students while those favoring a stronger practical and design orientation are likely to be "concerned" about the high proportion of these students.

The situation in engineering education posed by the high proportion of foreign graduate students is of more general interest to policymakers and practitioners in the field of international education because it constitutes the limiting case for testing assumptions about the impact of foreign students on U.S. higher education. Most immediately, however, the very high proportions of foreign engineering graduate students have been of growing concern to policymakers in government and higher education not simply because of consequences for the character and quality of engineering programs but also because of the significant role that engineering plays in underpinning the industrial strength of the United States. We shall deal with these concerns under the following rubrics:

(1) **Access to graduate engineering education.** The high proportion of foreign graduate students has caused concern about the extent to which these foreign students are "displacing" well-qualified U.S. students. At the undergraduate level, indeed, this concern led to the decision of the University of Illinois, in 1984, not to admit any more

foreign students to its B.S. program; and in California, the legislature has periodically asked engineering departments to justify enrollments of foreign students that exceed 25 percent. Our study will explore the state of applications for admission to graduate engineering programs as perceived by those most directly involved in graduate education, namely, departmental chairpersons and faculty. It attempts to answer the question: Does the presence of large numbers and proportions of foreign students have negative consequences for the quality of degree recipients? Are foreign graduate students displacing well-qualified U.S. graduate students in graduate engineering programs?

Access involves not simply admission to graduate engineering programs but also the necessary financial resources to pursue graduate studies. There are concerns about the extent to which foreign students are being subsidized through tax monies in public institutions and through private contributions in private ones. Our study will help illuminate the nature of the financial support provided to foreign students at the graduate level.

(2) The process and content of engineering education. In the last 25 years, there has been continuing discussion of the extent to which U.S. engineering graduate programs are capable of adjusting to the needs and expectations of foreign graduate students especially those who expect to return home. As the question is frequently put, are U.S. engineering curricula "relevant" to the needs of students from developing countries? For the most part, in spite of much discussion and argument about modifying U.S. engineering programs to provide a more relevant, responsive academic environment for foreign students, such modifications have generally not been made nor are they generally deemed desirable. Yet, as the proportion of foreign graduate students has grown, perspectives on the relevance issue have shifted drastically. Some engineering educators now voice concern about the possibile intrusion of developing-country problems into the training and research in U.S. engineering schools. The present study will shed some light on the extent to which foreign graduate students have, in fact, affected the process of teaching, the content of what is taught, and the characteristics of the research that is done.

(3) The quality of engineering education and research. There are various ways in which, potentially, the large proportion of foreign graduate students may affect the quality of engineering education. This may result, in part, from difficulties experienced by U.S. undergraduates who are taught by foreign teaching assistants with limited language facility; it may result, also, from the admission of foreign students with inadequate qualifications; or it may result from the burden that foreign graduate students place on the administration and the faculty of engineering schools. The study will show how these threats to quality are perceived, and if and insofar as they exist, what efforts are being made or suggested to deal with them.

At the same time, there has been concern about the consequences of the large proportion of foreign students for the quality of the research carried out in engineering schools. This problem may manifest itself in various ways: through the research skills and proclivities of the foreign students; through their relationships with engineering faculty; and through their restricted access to research that has national security implications. This study will address these concerns.

(4) National and economic security issues. The question has been raised in various quarters [e.g.,5] whether the education of foreign graduate students, as well as their participation in research, is consonant with U.S. foreign policy and economic objectives. The once-prevalent presumption that education in this country will enhance fruitful friendly relations with people in other countries and prove to be politically and economically rewarding has been partly replaced by concerns that there are risks in permitting foreign nationals access to scientific and technical information. This study does not attempt to assess the larger consequences for the generation of new knowledge of permitting or restricting the free flows of information [6], but it does reveal the extent to which research in engineering schools is affected by government or industrial concerns about the negative consequences of free flows. It does attempt to answer the question: Does the presence of foreign graduate students cause a significant problem for faculty involved in research projects that carry certain restrictions on grounds of national security or competitiveness?

Under the above four rubrics, the study explores the extent to which changes in the nature and quality of engineering education have taken place that can be attributed to the high proportion of foreign graduate students. Before this study was carried out, speculation was rife and facts were few about the impact of foreign graduate students. We can now provide information about the perceptions of the relative performance of U.S. and foreign teaching assistants and of the extent to which the presence of foreign graduate students affects the operation of U.S. engineering programs including defense-related research. Our data permit, then, some conclusions about the effects that these foreign graduate students have on the quality of instruction that takes place in engineering schools and on the characteristics of engineering research.

(5) The composition of faculty. It is not only among the graduate students in U.S. engineering programs that foreigners are conspicuous for their numbers and proportions. Among the faculty also there is a high proportion of individuals who are either foreign citizens or who were not born in the United States. In carrying out our study, we obtained some valuable data on the quantitative role of foreign-born faculty as well as some indication of the roles of these faculty members, primarily as they interact with foreign graduate students but also with regard to such matters as the extent of their involvement in externally-sponsored research.

Study design

In order to understand the perceptions of key staff of engineering schools, departmental chairpersons and faculty, in the fall of 1985, we surveyed these two groups with mail questionnaires. The chairpersons' questionnaire was sent to all chairpersons of departments or other entities that administer graduate degree programs in chemical engineering, civil engineering, electrical engineering, and mechanical engineering. Out of a total survey population of 651 chairpersons, 441 or 67.7 percent returned usable replies. The faculty questionnaire was sent to a probability sample estimated to be 14.6 percent of all faculty within the departments or other entities whose chairpersons were surveyed. In all, 1757 faculty questionnaires were mailed and 943, or 53.7 percent, usable responses were received. These response rates are high, overall; there was some variation among engineering disciplines, in that 47.2 percent of electrical engineering faculty responded, compared with 60.1 percent of chemical engineering faculty.

A two-stage probability sampling procedure was used for the faculty survey in which each individual faculty member had an equal probability of being selected. The faculty population was stratified along three variables: (1) the engineering discipline—chemical (ChE), civil (CE), electrical (EE), and mechanical (ME); (2) the form of university administration or governance (public/private); and (3) the institution's quality and/or research intensiveness (QRI). This latter index was developed as follows: two strata, QRI-1 and QRI-2, consisted of faculty in departments or programs that were rated in the top and bottom halves, respectively, of an assessment of U.S. research doctorate programs in engineering carried out under the aegis of the Conference Board of Associated Research Councils and published by the National Academy Press in 1982 [7]. A third stratum, QRI-3, was made up of faculty in those departments that were not included in the 1982 assessment but were listed in an American Society for Engineering Education (ASEE) directory of graduate programs published in March, 1985 [8]; their exclusion from the 1982 rankings could have been due to a number of factors, like the lack of doctoral programs, an insufficient number of doctorate recipients, or the recency of programs. In general, the QRI-3 programs are likely to be less research intensive than the QRI-1 or QRI-2 programs; it is difficult to make any judgments about the quality of the QRI-3 programs.

The questionnaires sent to chairpersons and faculty covered, in part, the same ground; both groups were surveyed with regard to the use of full-time foreign graduate students as teaching assistants and research assistants, the extent to which these foreign students are unable to participate in certain kinds of research because of security considerations, and the general issue of the extent to which foreign graduate students constitute an asset or a liability. In some respects, the two surveys were different, reflecting the different roles of chairpersons and faculty. Information and opinions were obtained from chairpersons about applications and admissions criteria and policies, student financiasl aid policies, and the rate of completion of degree programs of foreign and U.S. graduate students. Department heads also provided specific data about the number of foreign and U.S. graduate students in their departments (foreign students to be defined as full-time students on either temporary or permanent visas), the countries or places of origin of the foreign students, and the patterns of financial support of both the U.S. and the foreign group.

Faculty were questioned with regard to their experiences in teaching U.S. and foreign students and the extent of their continuing contacts with each group of students after degree completion. The faculty questionnaire contained a section designed to obtain a profile of faculty respondents.

Survey results

(1) Admissions and financial aid. Some 86.5 percent of the chairpersons of graduate departments or programs indicated that during the four years previous to our fall 1985 survey, there had been either a shortage of, or few if any, U.S. citizens applying for admission as full-time graduate students. Conversely, 86.1 percent reported a surplus or an adequate number of foreign applicants. These results vary somewhat among quality/research intensiveness strata but not dramatically so. Looking ahead to the next four years, 46.9 percent of the chairpersons expect no change in the number of U.S. applicants, 33.9 percent expect fewer, and 16.4 percent expect more. The judgments by chairpersons suggest that to maintain cohorts of well-qualified graduate students, it is essential to accept foreign citizens, and that there is no question of these foreign citizens "displacing" U.S. citizens.

Only a small percentage of all chairpersons, 14.9 percent, indicated that their department, school, or university has a policy that limits the percentage of foreign citizens admitted for graduate study to a specific maximum. In the case of QRI-1 chairpersons, the percentage reporting a "cap" was higher (32.1 percent) than in the other QRI categories, and in private institutions, only 7.1 percent of chairpersons reported an upper limit. This suggests that the highest-quality institutions are somewhat better able to recruit more high-quality U.S. students, and that there is less pressure in private than in public universities to limit the enrollment of foreign students. The mean limiting maximum percentage cited by the respondents is 30.5 percent.

The financial relationship between foreign students and their universities has two main aspects: the tuition and/or fees they are (or are not) charged and the extent and kinds of financial aid they receive. A small minority of institutions, 8.2 percent, charge foreign engineering students more than out-of-state U.S. students, and all the institutions that do so are public ones.

As regards financial aid, only 13.2 percent of chairpersons reported a policy limiting the amount or percentage of the total available financial aid that may be awarded to foreign graduate students. The restrictions varied: 39.3 percent of those reporting such a policy give some priority to U.S. citizens, and 24.6 percent will not support foreign citizens during their first year. Yet as indicated in Table 1, 44.3 percent of chairpersons indicated that an applicant's citizenship is a criterion of considerable importance in making financial aid awards. Indeed, when the chairpersons were confronted with the following hypothetical question, "If two graduate student applicants for financial aid from your department were judged to be of equal quality, and one was a U.S. citizen and the other a non-U.S. citizen, which one would be given preference?", the responses were as follows: 87.1 percent would give preference to the U.S. citizen, 11.3 percent would give preference to neither, and 0.2 percent would prefer the non-U.S. citizen. When the wording of the question was changed so that the non-U.S. citizen was described as having "slightly better qualifications for graduate study than a U.S. citizen," 56.9 percent would give preference to the U.S. citizen, 26.5 percent to the non-U.S. citizen, and 13.3 percent had no preference.

TABLE 1

CRITERIA USED BY CHAIRPERSONS IN MAKING FINANCIAL AID AWARDS

In making financial aid awards to **all** graduate student applicants, on a five-point scale from "strongly consider" (1) to "do not consider at all" (5), the following percentages of the total response indicated 1 or 2 for the following criteria:

CRITERIA	PERCENT OF TOTAL RESPONSE
GRE Scores	60.0
Undergraduate performance (grades)	93.9
Letters of recommendation	63.5
College or university where students did undergraduate work	72.3
Compatibility of applicants' research skills, etc. with department	70.9
The applicants' financial need	24.1
The applicants' citizenship	44.3

It would have been interesting to obtain responses to a hypothetical choice between a foreign student with markedly superior qualifications and a U.S. student. In any event, the responses we did obtain suggest that there is a certain disposition in engineering departments to use financial aid resources to encourage graduate study by U.S. students.

(2) The process and content of engineering education. According to surveyed chairpersons, 48.8 percent of full-time graduate students in the fall of 1985 were foreign, and faculty respondents estimated that they had, in the last four years, an average of 43.6 percent of foreign graduate students in their classes. In dealing with this high percentage of foreign students, 39.3 percent of faculty said they spent more time advising and assisting the typical foreign student than the typical U.S. student, and almost half of the faculty respondents made special efforts to accommodate the foreign students' difficulties in oral comprehension. A high proportion, 87.0 percent, had the same expectations for both foreign and U.S. students, and an even higher proportion, 96.5 percent, said they used the same standards in grading their graduate students, foreign or domestic.

Not only did faculty treat all students, foreign and domestic, the same in judging their performance, but faculty did not to any great extent take the national composition of their graduate students into account in defining the content of the subject matter to be taught. Only a very small proportion of faculty, 10.3 percent, indicated that they had tried to make teaching examples relevant to foreign students' backgrounds. Rather more, (20.6 percent), utilized foreign students as resources to illustrate international/comparative aspects of problems in classroom discussions. Yet these relatively small percentages indicate that, for better or worse, the high proportions of foreign students have not significantly affected the content of graduate engineering instruction.

(3) The quality of engineering education and research. Those who have misgivings about the impact of high proportions of foreign graduate students in engineering programs could very well be concerned, among other things, about changes in the quality of these programs. The findings of our study suggest that there are certain specific causes for concern, but that the overall situation is reassuring.

The responses obtained about admissions to engineering schools indicate that foreign students are absolutely essential to maintaining the quality of the student population; but for the availability of these foreign applicants, it is highly likely that U.S. applicants of lower quality than a particular institution normally accepts would have to be admitted. It is also clear from faculty responses that, by and large, foreign students are perceived as being competitive in most respects with U.S. students. As noted previously, most faculty have the same expectations of both groups and use the same standards in grading both. Three-fifths of faculty respondents, 60.6 percent, reject the idea that there is a specific maximum percentage of foreign students in a graduate course that should not be exceeded if their teaching is to be most effective. Among the minority of faculty who felt that some maximum is desirable, 55.3 percent set this maximum at 30 percent and another 37.0 percent felt that the maximum should be in the 31 to 50 percent range. These preferences, in the light of current actual enrollment figures, suggest that a significant minority of faculty have higher percentages of foreign students in their graduate-level courses than they consider optimal for effective teaching.

It is interesting to note here that U.S.-born and foreign-born faculty (the latter constitute 30.6 percent of all faculty) responded rather differently when asked about the amount of effort required to teach foreign students, the need to accommodate to their language difficulties, and the expectations of foreign students and standards used in judging U.S. and foreign students. Only 16.1 percent of foreign-born faculty felt that the teaching effort required for a foreign student was greater than for a U.S. student compared with 47.8 percent of U.S.-born faculty. Only 25.8 percent of foreign-born faculty, compared to 45.3 percent of U.S.-born faculty, indicated that, on average, they spent more time advising or assisting a typical foreign student than a typical U.S. student. Again, with regard to making special allowances for foreign students' language problems, 28.7 percent of foreign-born faculty thought this to be necessary compared to 38.7 percent of U.S.-born faculty. Hardly any U.S.-born faculty, 2.1 percent, indicated that in evaluating the work of foreign students, they expected more of them than of U.S. students while 14.9 percent of foreign-born faculty expected more of foreign students. Also, foreign-born faculty were less inclined to set a limit to the proportion of foreign graduate students in their courses.

These differences require cautious interpretation. They may have to do with the greater extent to which foreign-born faculty are able to identify or communicate with foreign students and with the foreign students' greater rapport with them, or with foreign-born faculty's greater disposition to be patient with the problems of foreign students, or with the greater ability of foreign-born faculty to appreciate the contributions of foreign students. At the same time, they may reflect a degree of ethnocentrism or racial bias on the part of U.S.-born respondents. Whatever the reason or reasons for the differences in judgments may be, such differences indicate that, at least in some respects, there is no simple and definitive assessment of the quality of foreign graduate students as students. They surely require a certain amount of extra instructional effort on the part of many faculty members, but there is nothing to suggest that the outcome of the greater teaching effort required for foreign graduate students is ultimately different from the outcome of the lesser effort required in some cases for their U.S. counterparts.

It is in two other areas, the instruction of undergraduate students by foreign teaching assistants and, to a lesser extent, the carrying out of research, that the high proportions of foreign graduate students appear to have some negative consequences.

(a) Foreign graduate students as teaching assistants. Teaching assistantships have two major purposes in graduate programs: they relieve faculty of some of the more routine instructional tasks, and they constitute a source of financial aid to graduate students. In engineering schools, therefore, teaching assistants (TAs) are used, whether or not there is a shortage of faculty. The recent shortage of full-time engineering faculty, which has been especially acute in electrical engineering, has led to greater than normal reliance on TAs. Among the chairpersons reporting a shortage of faculty, 31.6 percent indicated that they were hiring more TAs than they would prefer, and insofar as departments needed to rely on TAs, only 22.6 percent of responding chairpersons reported a sufficient pool of U.S. graduate students to meet departmental needs for TAs. This latter percentage was considerably higher for QRI-1 departments (38.9 percent) than for QRI-2 departments (17.1 percent) and slightly higher for private (26.4 percent) than for public (21.1 percent) institutions.

Large numbers of departments, then, must use foreign TAs. During the past four years, according to the chairpersons, the mean percentage of teaching assistantships awarded to foreign citizens was 46.7 percent; QRI-1 and QRI-2 programs had means of 40.2 percent and

51.6 percent, respectively. For those faculty who reported using teaching assistants at all, the mean percentage of teaching assistants who were foreign was 53.4 percent. For QRI-1 faculty, it was 50.0 percent compared with 59.5 percent for QRI-2 faculty; faculty in public institutions reported slightly larger percentages of foreign TAs than those in private institutions (54.0 percent vs. 52.0 percent) and mechanical engineering faculty somewhat larger percentages than chemical engineering faculty (56.7 percent vs. 47.5 percent). In 60.3 percent of the responding departments or programs, the foreign students who serve as teaching assistants are required to demonstrate English language proficiency above that required for admission; some 22 of 76 departments indicated that they do not award teaching assistantships to foreign students in their first year.

Based on the responses of faculty, it seems fair to say that the use of foreign TAs is not without problems. Faculty utilize both foreign and U.S. graduate students to perform a variety of TA functions, and for most of these functions, they prefer U.S. TAs over foreign TAs (see Table 2). The functions excepted from this preference are grading homework assignments and grading exams, for which "no preference" was the strongest response. In engineering courses, both of these functions are generally less highly dependent on the TAs' fluency in English than the other, more communication-dependent tasks listed in Table 2.

TABLE 2

FACULTY PREFERENCE FOR USING FOREIGN OR U.S. TEACHING ASSISTANTS.

	Prefer foreign TAs (%)	Prefer U.S. TAs (%)	No Preference (%)	Do not use TAs (%)
Grading homework	3.2	24.2	67.7	4.8
Grading exams	1.3	14.6	33.2	50.6
Giving lectures	1.0	39.3	11.7	47.4
Leading review sessions	0.8	43.0	31.4	24.8
Advising students	0.3	22.6	17.7	59.2
Conducting labs	1.3	46.5	36.2	15.6

When faculty were asked to compare the overall performance of U.S. and foreign graduate students as TAs, 59.6 percent responded that it was about the same, 32.5 percent thought the U.S. students performed better and 7.6 percent thought that foreign students performed better. Yet here again, there is a considerable difference between the judgments of foreign-born and U.S.-born faculty. Overall, 73.0 percent of foreign-born faculty considered the performance of foreign TAs to be about the same as that of U.S. TAs; 15.2 percent said the foreign students performed better and only 11.3 percent said they were worse. These responses differ substantially from those of the U.S.-born faculty, 43.2 percent of whom felt that the performance of foreign teaching assistants was not as good as that of U.S. TAs. These disparities raise the same kinds of questions as those suggested by discrepant judgments about foreign graduate students as students: Is the quality of performance as a teaching assistant to a significant extent a relative matter, dependent on certain characteristics of the faculty who are judging it? Does the quality of performance in fact vary, depending on the compatibility of faculty and teaching assistant?

A high proportion of faculty, 74.1 percent, thought that the main problem faced by foreign graduate students as TAs is that of English language proficiency. Other problems that also come up more frequently when foreign TAs rather than U.S. TAs are used are their lack of understanding of the U.S. undergraduate culture; their lack of familiarity with academic norms, for example, what constitutes cheating and plagiarism; and their inability to tell undergraduates what is expected of them (see Table 3).

TABLE 3.
Problems encountered by faculty more frequently with foreign than with U.S. teaching assistants.

Responses	Problem
305	They have problems communicating with undergraduates about their performance.
244	They do not understand U.S. undergraduate culture.
189	They are not familiar with academic norms, for example, cheating, and plagiarism.
179	They have problems telling undergraduates what is expected of them.
155	Undergraduates have complained about grades.
153	They have problems with laboratory sections.
150	Their expectations of undergraduates are too high.
124	They are too authoritarian with undergraduates.
119	Undergraduates have asked to be transferred out of their sections.
60	They are too permissive with undergraduates.
28	Their expectations of undergraduates are too low.

Total number of responses was 532.

More than half of the respondents thought that foreign TAs from Taiwan, the Peoples Republic of China, and India, in that order, were especially likely to encounter one or more of these problems. When asked the inverse question, almost 40 percent of faculty respondents indicated that their most effective TAs were likely to come from India, a strong first, followed by Taiwan and the United Kingdom. The fluency in English of TAs from India may give them a substantial advantage. This conclusion is suggested by the fact that when both faculty and chairpersons were queried in a more general way about the problems presented by foreign students, the problem mentioned most frequently by both groups was, by a large margin, language and communications (see Table 4).

TABLE 4.
Summary of responses regarding problems with foreign graduate students.

	Chairpersons		Faculty	
	Number	Percent	Number	Percent
Language; communication	323	34.32	714	44.15
Finances	149	15.83	121	7.48
Program; academic performance	130	13.81	269	16.63
Social/cultural	99	10.52	207	12.80
Lab, mechanical, design skills	63	6.69	115	7.11
Admissions	61	6.48	62	3.83
Departmental operations	45	4.78	32	1.98
No problems	24	2.55	55	3.40
Employment	24	2.55	21	1.29
Visa	23	2.44	21	1.29
TOTALS*	941	99.97**	1617	99.96

*Includes up to three responses per individual.
**Percentages may not add up to 100 due to roundoff errors.
Compiled by R. Torstrick

(b) Foreign graduate students as research assistants. Research assistantships are another important source of financial support for engineering graduate students, who play a very important part in research productivity. In engineering schools where faculty are able to maintain a flow of research grants and contracts, the doctoral research of the graduate students and much of the research carried out by candidates for master's degrees tends to be closely related to the research activities of the faculty. The skills of the graduate students as researchers and their compatibility with faculty, are likely to be important factors in the carrying out of research projects.

Information obtained from chairpersons indicates that, in the last four years, 48.5 percent of all research assistantships were awarded to foreign students; in QRI-1 institutions, the proportion was 44.7 percent and in QRI-2 institutions, 50.9 percent. Over 75% of the chairpersons reported that there were not enough U.S. graduate students to meet their departments' research assistantship needs. According to faculty, the shortage is even more acute. Overall, 87.6 percent of faculty reported a shortage of U.S. graduate students to serve as research assistants (RAs); even higher proportions of faculty in QRI-2 institutions reported shortages (93.2 percent, as against 84.0 percent for QRI-1 institutions) and by electrical engineering faculty (89.4 percent, as against 82.1 percent by those in chemical engineering.) Given this necessary heavy reliance on foreign RAs, it is important to ascertain whether, as perceived by faculty, they are more or less interchangeable with U.S. RAs or whether the use of these foreign RAs has any special advantages or disadvantages.

Many faculty do see differences between foreign and U.S. research assistants. In some respects, they attribute research interests to foreign RAs that differ from those of U.S. RAs. For example, 61 percent of faculty think that foreign graduate students are more theoretically oriented in their interests than U.S. graduate students, whereas less than 1 percent consider their research interests to be more experimental; only 4.3 percent believe them to be more oriented towards practical problems, while 33.4 percent see no real difference. There is some minor variation in these responses according to discipline: only 27.4 percent of chemical engineers and 27.7 percent of mechanical engineers see "no real difference," compared to 36.5 percent of chemical engineers and 40.0 percent of electrical engineers. Some 66.0 percent of chemical engineers and 67.8 percent of mechanical engineers find foreign students to be more theoretical, compared with 55.0 percent of chemical engineers and 57.0 of electrical engineers. We did not ask engineering faculty to provide us with judgments about the respective merits of the practical versus the theoretical orientations of U.S. and foreign graduate students, so it is not possible for us to come to conclusions about the extent to which the typical orientation of a U.S. student compared to a foreign student is likely to be congenial to faculty in specific disciplines or to engineering education in general. A further study will be required to probe these questions.

When faculty were queried about the specific research skills of U.S. and foreign RAs, their responses confirmed their judgements about the students' orientation on the theoretical - practical continuum (see Table 5).

TABLE 5

RESPONSE BY FACULTY TO THE QUESTION: FOR EACH OF THE FOLLOWING, WOULD YOU SAY THAT, IN GENERAL, U.S. STUDENTS HAVE MORE OF THE SKILLS NEEDED AS RESEARCH ASSISTANTS, FOREIGN STUDENTS HAVE MORE OF THE NECESSARY SKILLS, OR THERE ARE NO DIFFERENCES BETWEEN THE TWO GROUPS?

	More skills			
	U.S. students (%)	Foreign students (%)	No difference (%)	No judgement (%)
Design equipment	63.1	3.6	23.1	9.7
Run experiments	62.2	3.4	25.0	9.4
Record data	19.2	9.6	62.1	9.1
Analyze data with computers	19.5	18.4	56.1	5.8
Develop models	13.5	36.3	47.3	3.3
Write reports	72.0	3.2	23.0	1.8

Almost two thirds of the faculty attributed to U.S. students more of the practical skills needed for the tasks of designing experiments and running them. A total of 36.3 percent considered foreign students better at developing analytical and/or conceptual models, compared with only 13.5 percent who considered U.S. students to be better. Over half of those surveyed could see "no difference" between the skills of U.S. and foreign RAs in carrying out the tasks of recording data and analyzing data with the use of computers. As might be expected, the language problem surfaces again in regard to the skill in writing up research results: 72.0 percent of faculty think that U.S. students do this better. Since all the tasks mentioned above are important for getting research done, we might conclude that a certain mix of foreign and U.S. students is conducive to enhancing research productivity. But without entering the debate about the nature of engineering research and the balance between theory, experiment, and design, no clear conclusion can be drawn from our data about the optimal mix of foreign and U.S. students.

In some respects, faculty opinions about foreign RAs present a complex picture. Overall, 66.6 percent of the faculty respondents make a positive judgment about the assiduity of foreign RAs; they think that these RAs work harder than their U.S. counterparts. With regard to the substantive contributions of foreign RAs, about 30 percent of faculty see them as bringing fresh perspectives to problems, and about one-quarter indicated that foreign students had provided ideas for research areas. (We did not find out, unfortunately, to what extent faculty think they obtain such new perspectives and ideas from their U.S. RAs.) On the more negative side, about 30 percent of responding faculty think that it is more difficult, because of cultural differences, to establish a good working rapport with foreign students.

In these various judgments, yet again, there is some divergence between foreign-born and U.S.-born faculty; foreign-born tend to be more favorable than U.S-born faculty in assessing the research skills and performance of foreign graduate students. Thus, 83.2 percent of foreign-born faculty feel that foreign students work harder than U.S. students, compared with 57.9 percent of U.S.-born faculty; only 15.8 percent of foreign-born faculty feel that it is more difficult (because of cultural differences) to establish a good working rapport with foreign students, compared with 39.5 percent of U.S.-born faculty; and 91.7 percent of foreign-born faculty responded that foreign students have been either very important or somewhat important in their research over the past few years, while the corresponding percentage was 73.0 for U.S.-born faculty. It would be necessary to know more about the kind of research that faculty in each group are typically involved in to understand whether these differences have their basis in cultural identification and congeniality or in the substantive nature of the research.

Regardless of the differences between U.S.-born and foreign-born faculty, the judgments expressed by faculty in general, which point partly in positive and partly in negative directions, do not permit the simple conclusion that foreign research assistants are direct substitutes for U.S. research assistants. Each group appears to have advantages and disadvantages. If there were an adequate supply of each, what combinations of foreign and U.S. RAs would faculty in different engineering disciplines put together to optimize research productivity?

(4) National and economic security issues. From the perspective of this study, it is important to find out the extent to which the high proportion of foreign graduate students creates difficulties for carrying out research that is "sensitive" for reasons of U.S. national security or

U.S. economic competitiveness.

In quantitative terms, the effect of the exclusion of foreign students from certain projects seems relatively modest. About 12.6 percent of the chairpersons reported that in 1984 and 1985 some foreign students were unable to participate, on grounds of national security, in research programs available to U.S. graduate students (see Table 6). This percentage is higher for QRI-1 departments (14.2 percent) than QRI-2 departments (11.4 percent), for public (14.6 percent) than for private (7.8 percent) institutions, and for electrical engineering (19.0 percent) than for chemical engineering (7.4 percent) departments. Restriction of students on grounds of possible damage to economic competitiveness is even less common. In all the categories mentioned above, fewer than 10 percent of respondents answered affirmatively.

Some of this variation in the response rates to the question about the exclusion of foreign students on national security grounds might be related to the differential willingness of departments (or schools or universities) to accept contracts or grants for classified research, but this is a matter of speculation. Roughly a third of the respondents indicated that their acceptance of grants or contracts is governed by a policy that prohibits classified research. In QRI-1 programs, the proportion declining classified research is as high as 55.9 percent, and the proportion of private institutions adhering to this policy is higher than that of public ones (45.3 percent as compared to 27.0 percent). A very small percentage of departments (1.1 percent in total, 2.7 percent in QRI-1 institutions) have turned down research contracts because foreign students would not be able to participate in the research.

Among faculty, 12.4 percent reported that foreign graduate research assistants are either frequently or occasionally barred from access to laboratory equipment or information; 17.6 percent said that some funders prohibited them from using foreign students in research; and about one-quarter reported that some funders discouraged them from using foreign students (see Table 7). Some differences in these percentages appear across strata: for example, restrictions seem more prevalent in electrical and mechanical engineering than in civil and chemical engineering. Overall, 8.9 percent of faculty responded affirmatively when asked if the above restrictions or limitations had proven detrimental to their own research activities. Slightly higher percentages of QRI-1 (10.0 percent), private (10.2 percent), and electrical engineering (10.5 percent) faculty responded affirmatively to this question.

TABLE 6

CHAIRPERSONS' QUESTIONNAIRE: RESTRICTIONS ON FOREIGN ENGINEERING STUDENTS.

In 1984 and 1985, have any foreign graduate students in your department:

Been denied access, on grounds of **national security**, in any research programs available to U.S. graduate students?

	Total Response (%)	QRI-1 (%)	QRI-2 (%)	Public (%)	Private (%)	EE (%)	ChE (%)
Yes	3.7	7.1	3.8	4.2	2.3	5.1	1.0
No	95.9	92.9	96.2	95.5	96.9	94.0	98.9

Been unable to participate, on grounds of **national security,** in any research programs available to U.S. graduate students?

	Total Response (%)	QRI-1 (%)	QR1-2 (%)	Public (%)	Private (%)	EE (%)	ChE (%)
Yes	12.6	14.2	11.4	14.6	7.8	19.0	7.4
No	86.5	85.8	88.6	84.7	90.7	79.3	92.6

Been unable to participate on grounds **other than national security** (economic competitiveness, proprietary restrictions) in any research programs available to U.S. graduate students?

	Total Response (%)	QRI-1 (%)	QRI-2 (%)	Public (%)	Private (%)	EE (%)	ChE (%)	CE (%)
Yes	5.8	7.2	7.6	5.2	7.0	6.1	8.6	1.8
No	94.2	92.8	92.4	94.8	93.0	93.9	91.4	98.2

Have the above restrictions of limitations proven detrimental to your own research activities.

	Total Response (%)	QRI-1 (%)	QRI-2 (%)	QRI-3 (%)	Public (%)	Private (%)	ChE (%)	CE (%)	EE (%)	ME (%)
Yes	8.9	10.0	9.3	7.0	8.2	10.4	10.0	7.0	10.5	8.3
No	88.4	88.1	87.2	89.8	88.8	87.4	86.3	87.3	88.4	90.2

Interpretation of these findings is complicated. The proportion of faculty who see their research as being impeded by restrictions on foreign graduate students seems quite low and suggests that faculty are able to move their RAs around in such a way that it is the U.S. RAs who work on the restricted projects. But this may mean that the RAs best qualified to be involved in a particular project are not able to participate. Furthermore, though damage to some of the work of 8 to 10 percent of faculty seems a fairly limited amount, such a quantitative indicator does not provide insight into the importance of the research that cannot be carried out. Finally, our statistics cannot reveal the extent to which restrictions on the free flow of information lead to inhibitions on scientific and engineering creativity: if a particular line of investigation may be troublesome in that adequate research assistance may not be available, why not go in a different, but perhaps less valuable, direction?

TABLE 7

FACULTY RESPONSES TO THE QUESTION; HAVE YOU HAD ANY OF THE FOLLOWING EXPERIENCES DURING THE LAST FOUR YEARS IN CONNECTION WITH YOUR USE OF FOREIGN GRADUATE STUDENTS AS RESEARCH ASSISTANTS? (CIRCLE THE APPROPRIATE NUMBER FOR EACH STATEMENT):

Yes, Frequently, Or Upon Occasion

	Total Response (%)	QRI-1 (%)	QRI-2 (%)	QRI-3 (%)	PUBL (%)	PRIV (%)	CHE (%)	CE (%)	EE (%)	ME (%)
Restricted Access	12.4	8.21	3.0	18.1	12.0	13.3	8.9	6.0	13.6	18.0
Funding Source Prohibition	17.6	17.0	16.7	19.5	19.71	2.9	18.6	13.1	16.4	22.3
Funding Source Discouragement	24.9	23.7	26.5	24.6	26.9	20.1	23.5	20.2	26.1	28.1

(5) The composition of engineering faculty. We have shown above that the judgments by foreign-born faculty about foreign graduate students suggest that the interactions between these two groups are rather more positive than the interactions between the foreign graduate students and U.S.-born faculty. There are other findings as well that indicate that there are certain differences in the characteristics of foreign-born faculty and U.S.-born faculty; their impacts on engineering education and research may, therefore, be somewhat different also.

Some 30.6 percent of faculty were born outside the United States; this percentage is slightly lower in QRI-1 institutions (29.0 percent) and QRI-3 institutions (29.6 percent) than in QRI-2 institutions (34.5 percent). For faculty at private institutions, the mean percentage is 33.1 percent, as against 29.5 percent for public universities. Breaking the data down by discipline, chemical (24.8 percent) and civil (28.8 percent) engineering faculty have smaller proportions of foreign-born faculty than electrical (33.1 percent) and mechanical (32.0 percent) engineering faculty.

The mean age at which foreign-born faculty came to this country was 24.6 years while only 20.5 percent of foreign-born faculty indicated that they received their undergraduate education in the United States, at least 66 percent indicated that they received their graduate training in this country. This very high proportion of advanced degrees from U.S. institutions suggests that many foreign-born faculty are thoroughly familiar with U.S. graduate engineering programs, both their substantive requirements and their expectations of the appropriate roles of graduate students as teaching and research assistants.

Foreign-born faculty tend to be younger (mean age 44.2 years) than U.S.-born faculty (mean age 47.5 years). They also tend to be more research-intensive: 54.3 percent of foreign-born faculty devoted 26 percent or more of their time to externally sponsored research over the past three years compared with 41.7 percent of U.S.-born faculty. All apart from any special affinity between foreign-born faculty and foreign graduate students related to their common "foreignness" or to lingering faculty memories of what it is like to be a foreign student, it seems likely that the extent of involvement in research of foreign faculty requires their development of positive relationships with members of the large pool of foreign RAs.

Overall assessments

The significance of the participation of foreign students in U.S. higher education is often unexamined, as was shown by Craufurd Goodwin and Michael Nacht in their study of academic policymaking with regard to foreign students [1]. Although Goodwin and Nacht argue persuasively that the issue of foreign students deserves more attention on the part of academic planners and policymakers, such attention tends to emerge only in certain situations. One such situation exists when significant numbers of foreign students come from countries that are openly hostile to the United States as was the case with Iranian students a few years ago. Another situation occurs when in certain fields of study, like engineering or mathematics and computer science at the undergraduate level, foreign students compete directly with U.S. students for scarce places; in this situation, measures may be taken by at least some public institutions to limit severely the admission of foreign students or to exclude them altogether. Finally, it may happen that foreign students come to dominate enrollments in a particular field of study because a quite limited number of U.S. citizens are enrolling: that is the current situation in graduate engineering education. When foreign students approach parity with or even outnumber U.S. students, this is a quite unusual state of affairs, and there is a strongly felt need to assess its various consequences. Our study is an attempt to do so.

Our particular focus in this study has been on the consequences of high proportions of foreign graduate students for engineering education and research, and for this reason, we have sought judgments from those most qualified to provide information and opinions about these particular consequences, the departmental chairpersons and faculty of engineering programs. We found that both chairpersons and faculty report varied experiences with foreign graduate students: in some respects, many chairpersons and faculty perceive foreign and U.S. graduate students to be more or less interchangeable, while in other respects, the "foreignness" of the foreign students is of some significance. This foreignness, in turn, has both positive and negative implications.

On the positive side, chairpersons attest to the immense importance of foreign graduate students in maintaining the quality as well as the very viability of programs; given the current limited supply of well-qualified U.S. students, the supply of foreign graduate students appears to be an essential element. Faculty, similarly, acknowledge the important contributions that foreign graduate students make to their research; and some oven derive a kind of personal satisfaction from teaching foreign students that differs from the satisfaction of teaching U.S. students.

But there is also some evidence that, even if quality is not a factor, chairpersons do not regard foreign and U.S. students as interchangeable in the admissions process; they express a certain preference for awarding financial aid to U.S. students, even if these students are not quite as well qualified as the foreign ones. Chairpersons also generally consider foreign graduate students to be a greater administrative burden than U.S. students. Similarly, faculty tend to find that teaching foreign students requires greater effort and they appear to parcel out teaching assistant tasks in such a way as to take into account the potential impact of the heterogeneous backgrounds of foreign TAs, i.e. their language problems and cultural differences, on the undergraduates with whom they are in contact. There is, certainly, a negative side. How serious the negative impacts of foreign graduate students are remains a matter of debate: perceptions vary, depending on the national origin of the faculty members whose judgments we solicited.

Overall, from the point of view of both chairpersons and faculty, foreign graduate students are more of a boon than a bane. To put it another way, foreign graduate students, at the present time, appear to be a solution to the troubles that afflict engineering education, rather than a problem. Given the acute dearth of U.S. graduate students, the substitution of foreign for U.S. students makes it possible for U.S. engineering schools, in the aggregate, to pursue their objectives, namely instruction (at both the undergraduate and graduate levels) and research, at steady or even growing levels and in a reasonably predictable manner.

As indicated by our data, foreign graduate students are a satisfactory substitute for U.S. students, but not an exact equivalent. They are less effective in some respects, especially because of communications difficulties. They are more effective in other respects, partly, perhaps, because of their cultural backgrounds, which appear to dispose some of them to great diligence, and partly because of their educational backgrounds, which provide in many instances a high level of theoretical sophistication. When asked to strike a balance, roughly two-thirds of chairpersons believe that foreign graduate students have positive effects on their departments. When the question was put to them whether foreign students were an asset, 54.2 percent said that they are, while only 7.9 percent considered them a liability. When faculty were asked to make such an overall assessment of foreign graduate students, the breakdown of their opinions was very similar to that of chairpersons; roughly two-thirds indicated that they saw positive effects, while only one-third thought that the presence of foreign graduate students had some negative effects on their departments. When the question was couched in terms of assets vs. liabilities, about 59 percent of faculty felt that foreign students are an asset; only 10.7 percent thought that they are a liability. QRI-1 faculty (66.2 percent) were more favorable that QRI-2 (49.7 percent) faculty, and faculty in private institutions (64.0 percent) were more favorable than those in public institutions (56.8 percent).

It seems very likely, for reasons that will be dealt with further below, that, in the best of all worlds, in which there is an abundant supply of well-qualified U.S. graduate students, both the chairpersons and faculty of engineering programs would be disposed to diminish the proportion of foreign graduate students. But the fact that high proportions of foreign engineering students are considered anomalous, while high proportions of U.S. students are seen as "normal," may lead to a certain inclination to focus on the problems caused by foreign students in engineering.

Policy implications

The high proportion of foreign graduate students in engineering programs raises policy issues of several different kinds. At the simplest level, perhaps, there is the question of the effective operation of these engineering programs as educational and research enterprises. Beyond this, there is the question of the role the graduates of advanced engineering programs play in the human resource needs of the United States and of other countries. Further, there is the question of the use and usefulness of the knowledge generated in engineering schools in the military and commercial efforts of the United States and of the many countries in the world with which it has either friendly or antagonistic relationships. Our study provides policy guidance with regard to some aspects of these issues.

(1) Implications for engineering education and research. The inclination on the part of some chairpersons of engineering departments and of a good many faculty to prefer U.S. graduate students may be, to some extent, a matter of avoiding certain administrative burdens: the need to ensure compliance with visa requirements by foreign students, to deal with their communications problems, and to surmount the problems caused by their ineligibility to participate in defense-related research. It is simply easier to run engineering programs when there is a clear sense of the students' ability and eligibility to participate in instruction and research. However, this preference may also have other sources. It may be based on real concerns about the effects foreign graduate students have on the quality of education both at the graduate and the undergraduate level; it may be related to the sense that foreign graduate students, by virtue of their research interests, exert a certain undesirable pressure on the direction of the research carried on in engineering schools; it may be due to concerns, real or imagined, about the effects of the large proportion of foreign students on the dispositions of those who make decisions about the funding of engineering training and research; it may be due to realistic concerns about the stability of the flow of graduate students into engineering schools; and finally, it may be due to nationalistic sentiment in a world of nation-states.

Each of these concerns deserves scrutiny by policymakers and practitioners (in this context, chairpersons and faculty are key practitioners). With regard to the question of the quality of engineering education, our study suggests that foreign graduate students are quite satisfactory as students, but that they may be somewhat less satisfactory as teaching assistants and may, therefore, have a negative impact on undergraduate engineering education. This problem may be dealt with in various ways: by closer scrutiny of the language capability of foreign teaching assistants and remedial language instruction for those who need it; greater efforts to sensitize foreign graduate students to the norms of the academic culture of U.S. universities in general and engineering schools in particular; and perhaps by some attempts to give undergraduates the sense that, on the one hand, their difficulties are real and legitimate, while, on the other hand, they also may be able to ease these difficulties by focusing on the positive qualities of their teaching assistants rather than on the impenetrability of their accents.

The question of the effect of the research orientation of foreign graduate students on the research enterprise of engineering schools and, therewith, on the overall health of U.S. industrial activity, is a more elusive one. To understand this effect more thoroughly, it would be desirable to go beyond the scope of our study and to explore in greater depth the characteristics of the research being carried on by engineering faculty in general and by faculty in different kinds of schools and in different disciplines. Such an exploration would make it possible to come to conclusions about the extent to which the theoretical orientation of foreign graduate students is congenial with faculty research interests or goes against the grain. It might then be possible, also, to match more closely the research orientations of faculty and of those students, whether U.S. or foreign, who are admitted for graduate study in a given field. A recent article in the *Technology Review*[10] indicates that there are certainly some engineering faculty who find the increasingly theoretical orientation of engineering education and research an unfortunate development. If, in fact, as Kerr and Pipes argue, engineering graduate education has become too theoretical, and if it were desirable to move in a more "hands-on" design direction, some adjustments would be required of foreign graduate students.

From the point of view of chairpersons and faculty of engineering programs, the legitimacy of their activities in the eyes of those who provide financial support is, of course, of great importance. Our study provides little direct evidence about the extent to which the high proportion of foreign graduate students damages this legitimacy. Yet the preference shown for U.S. students may well indicate a sensitivity to the fact that in a world made up of nation-states, it is not unreasonable for student-citizens of the country in which institutions of higher education reside to be viewed as the primary clients to be served and supported. Some universities serve regional or U.S. state roles which further focus their priority clientele. It is certainly extreme to resent all subsidization with taxpayers' monies of foreign students or even of students from out of state, but it is not extreme to be concerned that the funding sources (those whose mission is not explicitly targeted towards the development of poor countries) might become alienated if financial resources are used primarily to train foreign students. The high proportion of foreign students may well come to jeopardize the support of teaching and research activities by legislators, trustees, and public or private funding agencies that are responsive to the sentiments of those who give priority to national and local interests. Yet decisions about the desirable composition of this particular graduate student population go beyond the educational sphere; they affect the supply of needed professional personnel to U.S. industry and U.S. academic institutions. At the present time, at least, both industry and engineering education would suffer severe personnel shortages if engineering schools were not training foreign graduate students, a high proportion of whom, roughly half according to a study focused on the 1980-82 time period, ultimately obtain employment in the United States [11].

Finally, in the educational sphere, there is the question of the stability of engineering education which depends centrally on the supply of well-qualified graduate students. Our study shows that the supply of U.S. students alone would be far from sufficient to permit engineering programs to continue in their present form or perhaps for some to continue at all. (We shall suggest below some possible reasons why U.S. students are not, at the present time, pursuing graduate studies in engineering.) Foreign students are essential if the training of undergraduates is to be possible, since at the present time, there are simply not enough U.S. teaching assistants. They are essential, likewise, if research is to be done at current levels, since there are not enough U.S. research assistants. Yet this situation might well move policymakers to consider ways to increase the supply of U.S. graduate students in engineering. The present stability of engineering programs, dependent as it is on foreign students, may be precarious. What if these large student flows were to diminish? A large percentage of foreign graduate students come from three places: Taiwan, India, and the People's Republic of China. It is at least possible that these Asian students may find it increasingly attractive to study elsewhere; for Indian students, it may become increasingly possible to obtain high-quality training in their home country. In any event, a sudden, or even a gradual, reduction in the influx of students could cause considerable difficulty.

It is not altogether clear what can be done to induce more U.S. students who have obtained B.S. degrees to undertake graduate studies in engineering. The conventional wisdom is that it is not an economically sound decision for them to do graduate work, given their access to well-paying jobs and the income they would have to forego. It has been suggested also that the federal government's shift from the support of graduate fellowships in engineering to the support of research assistantships has made it easier for faculty to provide financial assistance to foreign graduate students [12]. Furthermore, it is possible that the attractive opportunities offered by industry for part-time graduate study, at the company's expense, is deflecting some young engineers from continuing on to doctoral programs.

The kinds of questions to be explored are then: Would generous fellowships make an important difference? Would vastly increased starting salaries for doctoral degree recipients make a difference? In other words, how central are economic factors in the decisions to go or not to go to graduate school. And how important may be other factors like the kind of undergraduate institution the students attend or the students' socioeconomic background. And if economic inducements are not the answer, what else can be done to recruit more U.S. citizens? (The authors of this report are about to undertake a further study that examines the factors in the decisions of engineering undergraduates and of those who are already in graduate school with regard to the perceived rewards, or lack of them, of advanced degrees, as well as the characteristics of the students who do and do not choose graduate study.)

(2) Implications for the supply of professional personnel. Although our study focussed immediately on the impact of foreign graduate students on engineering education, the relationship between education and employment in engineering is so close that it is appropriate to give at least some attention to the policy implications of the high proportion of foreign graduate students for the supply of engineers with advanced degrees to the U.S. labor market. We have suggested above that engineering education might benefit in certain ways from a change in the balance between U.S. and foreign graduate students. Should the same issue be raised in connection with the flow of foreign recipients of advanced engineering degrees into the U.S. labor market?

The research by Michael Finn of Oak Ridge Associated Universities [11] shows clearly that foreign recipients of advanced degrees in science and engineering are in demand by U.S. industry and U.S. academia. In 1982, although only 6.0 percent of all employed scientists and engineers with doctoral degrees and 5.3 percent of those with master's degrees were foreign nationals, 50 percent of those on temporary visas who obtained PhD degrees in engineering and computer science in 1980-81 (and 62 percent of those on temporary and permanent visas) were employed in this country. Given the cumbersome bureaucratic procedures that employers have to go through in order to demonstrate their need for these foreign citizens, it seems highly unlikely that they would be hiring foreign engineers if they were not, indeed, the best-qualified individuals for the available jobs. According to Finn, the largest number of foreign scientists and engineers are employed in business and industry and the next largest number in 4-year colleges and universities. Our own study indicates that currently about one-third of engineering school faculty are foreign-born (we did not find out whether or not individuals had been naturalized), and the overwhelming majority of them received their advanced degrees in the United States.

The obvious demand for these foreign recipients of U.S. advanced degrees should lay to rest any concerns about the displacement of U.S.

citizens. The more urgent question may be whether U.S. industry and U.S. academia have become too dependent on these foreign scientists and engineers. Once again, as in the case of graduate programs in engineering, it seems appropriate to ask: What if foreign nationals ceased coming? What if the economic situation in their home countries changes in such a way as to make it advantageous for them to return home? In industry, they constitute only 3.5 percent of all professional employees, so that in quantitative terms, at least, they would not leave a very large hole, but it has been suggested (for example, by Dr. Peter Cannon, chief scientist at Rockwell International) that in qualitative terms, in particular specialized areas, they are of very central importance [13]. In engineering schools, the ranks of assistant professors aged 35 years or less would be reduced by one-half if those from other countries suddenly disappeared [14], and our study shows that foreign-born faculty (who tend to be younger than U.S.-born faculty) are more involved in research. In engineering schools then, foreign faculty are highly important both quantitatively and qualitatively [15].

It seems, then, that the high proportions of foreign graduate students in engineering programs (and some science programs) has spill-over effects in the U.S. labor market for highly-trained individuals, and that policymakers might well consider appropriate ways of making the job situations, whether in industry or academia, more attractive to U.S. citizens who obtain advanced degrees in engineering.

(3) Implications for national security and commercial competition. We shall consider, finally, what foreign engineering graduate students mean for broader U.S. national interests especially with regard to national security and U.S. trade. Engineering education and research are in a very special position vis-a-vis the U.S. economy and other U.S. national interests. While basic science may, in the long run, be just as important if not more so to economic growth and national defense, the results of engineering research are often more visibly and palpably relevant to these crucial concerns, and, correspondingly, relevant also to the economic and military objectives of other countries. Present trends toward closer government-university-industry cooperation could increase the real or apparent commercial or military value of engineering research. In this situation, it may be especially threatening to be heavily dependent on foreign students to keep engineering education and research functioning effectively. Even if all of these foreign students come from "friendly" countries, they are not perceived to be the same as U.S. students. In fact, they come, for the most part, from countries that are at present time relatively friendly, but this situation could change. And, as already noted in connection with the educational and labor market implications of foreign students, there is always the possibility that for political or economic reasons they might not come here at all and leave the U.S. engineering research enterprise in serious difficulty.

Policymakers must balance a number of considerations in dealing with the implications of the participation of foreign students in research that bears on national security and economic competition. They need to weigh the importance of "secure" research against the importance of open research, keeping in mind not only that openness is an essential characteristic of U.S. universities and of effective scientific endeavors, but also that many foreign students — perhaps a majority of them — come here because they are attracted by the openness of our society and the opportunities it offers as well as by the quality of our educational institutions and may remain and become U.S. citizens making important contributions. They have to consider the immediate obstacles to ongoing research that are created by the exclusion of foreign students in relation to the remote possibility that participation by foreign students will damage U.S. national interests. They need to take into account the advantages of having foreign students take our civilian technologies back to their home countries and build trade relations on such shared technologies, as well as the risk that eventually foreign countries may develop autonomous, competitive economies based on these technologies.

In this area of policymaking, the large number of foreign students makes the problem of security more visible though it may not really increase its seriousness. Damage can be done and has been done by one or a few committed individuals who have not been foreign students. The high numbers and proportions of foreign graduate students should cause more concern because excessive dependency on foreign students is, per se, not in the U.S. national interest, rather than because of serious danger that open access to university engineering research will be abused. However, should such research shift strongly towards defense-related and economically proprietary activity, then the situation will require reappraisal.

(4) Conclusion. High proportions of foreign graduate students are, at the present time, essential to the operation of U.S. engineering programs, but they also render these programs vulnerable. This suggests that energetic efforts should be made to shift the proportions between U.S. and foreign graduate students towards a greater involvement of U.S. students. To reduce dependency on foreign graduate students, it is necessary to understand more deeply the reasons for the present situation and especially the reasons why foreign students and U.S. students, respectively, do and do not pursue graduate studies in engineering.

We are not recommending any drastic steps to change the composition of the graduate student body in engineering programs. Foreign graduate students and foreign-born faculty have clearly made invaluable contributions in this area and will continue to do so. Any effort to restrict severely the entry of foreign students could have serious negative consequences for engineering programs and to a lesser degree for certain components of the U.S. labor force. Furthermore, there are serious moral questions that arise should a country and a profession that have relied upon and welcomed immigrants through the years decide to change policy. We would like to indicate , simply, that differences in language, differences in styles of research, and differences in primary national allegiance can become burdensome when the proportions of foreign graduate students in engineering education is very high. The advantages of a foreign component in the student body may well be undermined when the proportion of foreign students is one half or more [16].

References and Notes

1. Goodwin, Craufurd and Michael Nacht, *Absence of Decision*, Institute of International Education, 1983.

2. Solmon, Lewis C. and Betty J. Young, *The Foreign Student Factor,* Institute of International Education, 1987.

3. For a review of some of these issues, see Barber, E.G. and R.P. Morgan, "Engineering Education and the International Student: Policy Issues", *Engineering Education* (April 1984) pp. 655-659. For another publication of the results of this study see Barber and Morgan, "The Impact of Foreign Graduate Students on Engineering Education in the United States," *Science,* Vol. 236 (3 April 1987), pp. 33-37.

4. "Foreign Citizens in U.S. Science and Engineering: History, Status and Outlook," prepared by National Science Foundation, Washington, D.C., (November, 1985) p. 157. Note that the NSF figures differ somewhat from those reported annually by the American Society for Engineering Education (ASEE).

5. "Quality in Engineering Education", *Engineering Education* ,Vol 77, No. 1, (October 1986) pp. 16-24, 49-50.

6. Schrage, M., "Why Subsidize Importers? Foreigners Use Our Universities to Bury Our Industry," *Washington Post,* (June 1 1986).

7. Jones, L.V., G. Lindzey, and P.E. Coggeshall, Eds., "An Assessment of Research-Doctorate Programs in the United States: Engineering," National Academy Press, Washington, D.C. (1982).

8. "Engineering College Research and Graduate Study", *Engineering Education* , Vol 75, No. 6, (March 1985).

9. For a further discussion of the pros and cons of controls on university research, see "Scientific Communication and National Security", Na-

tional Academy Press (1982). This report, prepared by a National Academy of Sciences and National Academy of Engineering Panel headed by Dale Corson, president-emeritus of Cornell University, recommends that there be no restrictions of any kind limiting access or communications to either basic or applied university research unless it involves a technology meeting very specific criteria (e.g., government supported research that will lead to military products in a short time should be classified; some restrictions on participation by nationals of designated foreign countries in narrowly delineated "gray areas" of research are deemed appropriate.)

10. Kerr, Arnold D. and R. Byron Pipes, "Why We Need Hands-On Engineering Education," *Technology Review,* Vol. 90, No. 7 (October, 1987) pp. 36-42.

11. Finn, M.G., "Foreign National Scientists and Engineers in the U.S. Labor Force, 1972-1982," Oak Ridge Associated Universities report ORAU-244, available from NTIS, Springfield, VA, 22161 (June 1985).

12. Finn, M.G., paper delivered at the Workshop on International Movement of Engineers, National Academy of Sciences, Washington, D.C., July 7, 1987.

13. Cannon, Peter, paper delivered at the Workshop on International Movements of Engineers, National Academy of Sciences, July 7, 1987.

14. Falk, Charles, paper delivered at the Workshop on International Movements of Engineers, National Academy of Sciences, July 7, 1987.

15. See *Science and Government Report* Vol. XVII, No. 8 (May 1, 1987) p. 4. As reported in this newsletter, an NSF study entitled "Future Costs of Research: the Next Decade for Academe" indicates that immigration will probably only partly ease the expected shortages of academic faculty.

16. Barber, Elinor G., Morgan, Robert P., and Rebecca Torstrick, "Foreign Graduate Students in U.S. Engineering Programs: Problems and Solutions," *Engineering Education,* Vol. 78, No. 3 (December, 1987).

17. Acknowledgements. We thank A. Abdallah, B. Barber, T. Bergeron, S. Berhorst, W. Darby, T. Feichtinger, M. Glassman, M. Golladay, C. Partain, J. Paules, A. Russo, E. Singer, D. Strickland, R. Torstrick, D. Williams, and P. Yee for their contributions, and members of our project advisory committee for their time and assistance. We thank the engineering faculty and chairpersons who completed questionnaires. Supported by National Science Foundation grant SR-8315308.

IIE RESEARCH SERIES

Readers of this IIE Research Report may be interested in earlier titles in the series. They are available through the Educational Resources Information Center (ERIC) Clearinghouse on Higher Education, One Dupont Circle, NW, Suite 630 Washington DC 20036-1183.

Additional single copies of this report can be ordered directly from IIE if accompanied by a check for $4.00 for postage and handling. Orders should be directed to:
Publications Service
Institute of International Education
809 United Nations Plaza
New York, NY 10017

Report #7
FOREIGN STUDENT FLOWS:
Their Significance for American Higher Education
Elinor G. Barber, Editor

Report #8
A SURVEY OF POLICY CHANGES:
Foreign Students in Public Institutions of Higher Education 1983- 1985
William Mc Cann Jr.

Report #9
DECLINE AND RENEWAL:
Causes and Cures of Decay Among Foreign-Trained Intellectuals and
Professionals in the Third World
Craufurd D. Goodwin
Michael Nacht

Report #10
CHOOSING SCHOOLS FROM AFAR:
The Selection of Colleges and Universities in the United States By Foreign Students
Marianthi Zikopoulos
Elinor G. Barber

Report #11
THE ECONOMICS OF FOREIGN STUDENTS
Stephen P. Dresch

Report #12
THE FOREIGN STUDENT FACTOR:
Their Impact on American Higher Education
Lewis C. Solmon
Betty J. Young

Report #13
INTERNATIONAL EXCHANGE OFF- CAMPUS:
Foreign Students and Local Communities
Mark Baldassare
Cheryl Katz

Report #14
MENTORS AND SUPERVISORS:
Doctoral Advising of Foreign and U.S. Graduate Students
Nathalie Friedman